I would like to thank my husband and family for their support and unwavering believe in me, my amazingly wonderful children who teach me so much every day, especially Ava, who provided me with the inspiration to write this book. Finally, I would like to thank many of my friends who have joined me on the personal development journey, especially those who were there at times of great need, you all know who you are. Without you I would not be where I am today.

I would also like to dedicate this book in memory of two very special people who inspired me, but are, sadly, no longer with us.

# This book belongs to

...........................................................

...........................................................

# Ava the Mermaid

Written by Eleanor Baggaley

Illustrated by Jenn Garside

Say hello to Ava the Mermaid.

Ava loves to swim in the ocean;
she likes watching the seahorses dance
and the dolphins play.

Ava is just like the other mermaids in her part of the ocean, except that she has something extra special...

...You have to look very carefully to notice but Ava's tail is a little bit shorter and she has an extra colour in her scales. Everyone else has just two colours but Ava has three colours; blue, yellow and green.

Ava longs to swim with the other mermaids and mermen.

The other mermaids and mermen don't understand why Ava's tail looks different from theirs, and they just don't know if it's ok to ask her about it.

Ava can't swim as fast as they can and they don't know if playing with Ava would spoil their games.

They don't really know how to help Ava to join in.

Ava's sister and brother help Ava learn to swim every day; she holds onto their tails to swoosh through the water. They teach her how to roly-poly in the water and do other tricks.

When Ava learns to roly-poly by herself her whole family laugh and smile with pride. The extra colours in Ava's tail make fantastic patterns in the water.

One day when Ava was out swimming with her sister and brother, she met another beautiful mermaid, called Betsy, who also had three colours in her tail. The pattern was different from Ava's but still just as beautiful.

Betsy joined Ava, her sister and her brother. They played games together, swooshing around the water, making patterns and learning tricks. Ava was so pleased to have a new friend.

The next day, when Ava was out swimming with Betsy, the other mermaids and mermen came by.

They were amazed at how well Ava and her friend could roly-poly. They asked Ava and Betsy if they could join in and play together.

Ava told the group how her sister and brother taught her the tricks and how they help her swim faster through the water.

Ava explained that she sometimes struggles to keep up because her tail fins are a bit shorter than theirs but she still enjoys playing games.

Once the other mermaids and mermen knew how they could help Ava and Betsy swim, they invited them to join in their games.

They loved all of the new tricks that Ava and Betsy were able to teach them.

# What do you struggle with sometimes?
## Who helps you out?

..................................................

..................................................

..................................................

..............................................

........................................

....................................

..................................

..............................

# I'm good at:

...............................................................

...............................................................

...............................................................

...............................................................

...............................................................

...............................................................

...............................................................

...............................................................

# What do you do to help other people?

........................................................

........................................................

........................................................

........................................................

........................................................

........................................................

........................................................

........................................................

........................................................

# I enjoy . . .

...................................................

...................................................

...................................................

...................................................

...................................................

...................................................

...................................................

...................................................